Written by Gerald Hacker & Andrew Wolthers
Illustrated by Ryan Adamson

Edited by Rachelle Burk & Sara Hays

Copyright © 2012
GameRules4Kids.com • Birmingham, AL

Published by **GAMERULES**

ISBN: 978-0-9882895-2-9

End Zone

Team Area

STALLIONS

-01 -02 -08 -0₺ 05 0

Fifty
Yard Line
(Mid-Field) →

Yardage Markers ↙

-10 -20 -30 -40 50 4

Goal Line ↗

Team Area

2 • FOOTBALL FIELD DIAGRAM •

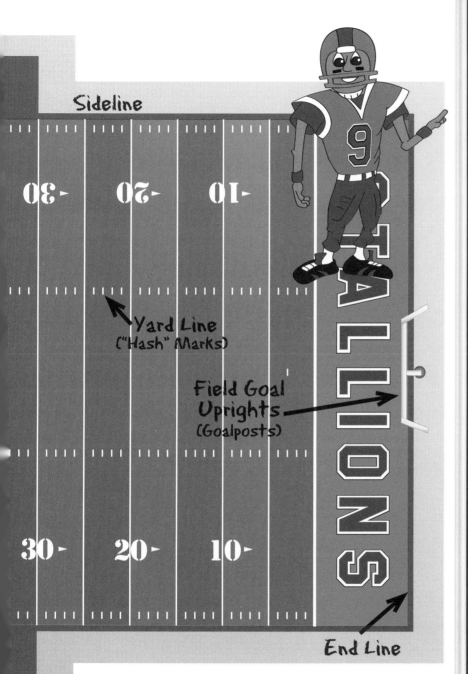

Sideline

30 **20** **10**

Yard Line
("Hash" Marks)

Field Goal
Uprights
(Goalposts)

30- 20- 10-

End Line

Frankie stood with his teammates near the goal line.
We can still do this, he thought. His heart pounded as the fans cheered from the stands.

Frankie knew this was a critical moment in the game, and he knew what he had to do. He got in his stance. Ready....Set....

Earlier that day...

Frankie and the rest of the Stallions stood together on the sideline. Coach Johnson gathered the players together before the opening **kickoff**. "Boys, the Bandits are a very good team. We need to play hard on both **offense** and **defense** today," he said.

A **KICKOFF** is used at the start of each game, after halftime, or to resume play after a team scores. During a kickoff, the ball is usually placed on a tee and kicked down the field to the other team by the team's *Kicker*.

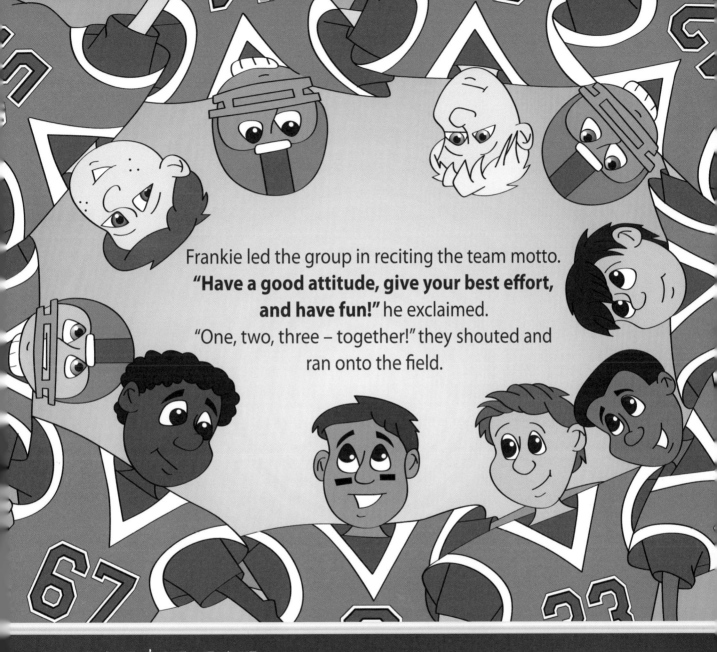

Frankie led the group in reciting the team motto. **"Have a good attitude, give your best effort, and have fun!"** he exclaimed.
"One, two, three – together!" they shouted and ran onto the field.

OFFENSE & DEFENSE are the terms used to describe each team on the field. The team that has the ball and is trying to score is on offense, while the team on defense tries to prevent the offensive team from scoring.

Frankie was one of the Stallions' best players. Not only did he play on offense and defense, but he also played on **Special Teams**. The **referee** blew the whistle to start the game.

WHOOSH! The ball was in the air. Frankie followed the ball as it dropped into his hands. *Now run*, he thought!

SPECIAL TEAMS are the groups of players that play on kicking plays such as kickoffs. Players who play on special teams usually play on offense and defense as well.

Frankie sprinted toward the sideline and then cut back to the middle of the field. A player from the Bandits reached out and made the **tackle**. The whistle blew and Frankie was **down**.

THE REFEREE starts and stops each play by blowing his whistle.
A TACKLE is used by the defensive team to stop the player with the ball. Once the offensive team is tackled and ruled **DOWN**, they have to re-group and run another play.

Cornerback

Safety

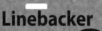
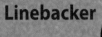

Linebacker

Linebacker

The Stallions were ready to play offense. They lined up in their **positions**. Frankie was a **running back**, and his friend Seth played **quarterback**. The rest of the team lined up as **linemen**, **wide receivers** and a **tight end**.

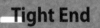

Tight End **Tackle** **Guard**

Wide Receiver

Offensive Linemen

Running Back

POSITIONS

Cornerback

Safety

Defensive
Linemen

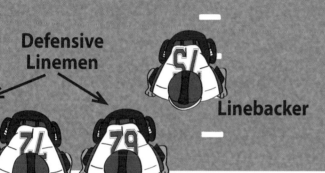

Linebacker

The Bandits also took their positions
on defense as **linemen**, **linebackers**,
cornerbacks and **safeties**.

Guard   Tackle

Wide
Receiver

Center

Wide
Receiver

Quarterback

Seth reached under the center to take the **snap**.

"Hut, hut!" he shouted. The center snapped the ball to start the play.

A SNAP is the way an offensive play is started in football. The center typically takes the ball off the ground and passes it backwards through his legs to the quarterback. A *shotgun* snap is used when the quarterback is several steps behind the linemen and the center throws the ball through his legs to the quarterback.

Seth spun around and handed the ball to Frankie on a **rushing** play. Frankie saw an opening in the defense and sprinted through it. The Bandits' linebacker tackled him but only after Frankie had gained 15 yards!

A RUSHING play is also called a running play and happens when an offensive player tries to run the ball forward and gain yards "on the ground." Quarterbacks, running backs, and wide receivers are normally the players who carry the ball on rushing plays.

"**First down**!" signaled the referee.

"Nice run, Frankie," said Seth as they came back to the **huddle**. One of their teammates ran in from the sideline with a new play.

A FIRST DOWN happens when a team gains 10 yards or more on offense. A team will have four plays (downs) to get a first down; otherwise, the defensive team will get the ball back.

"Split right – Z Streak," said Camden. Frankie looked wide-eyed at Seth and grinned. He knew this play meant the ball was coming to him. The team broke the huddle and approached the **line of scrimmage**.

A **HUDDLE** is when the players on the field gather together and talk about what play they are about to run. In an offensive team huddle, players will also decide when the center is supposed to snap the ball – also called a *snap count*.

THE LINE OF SCRIMMAGE is the imaginary line where the ball is snapped, extending from sideline to sideline.

Seth received the snap. Frankie darted out of the backfield and up the sideline looking for a **pass**.

In a PASS or a *forward pass*, the player with the ball throws it forward to one of his teammates. The offensive team is only allowed one forward pass on every play from the line of scrimmage, and the ball must be thrown from behind the line of scrimmage.

Seth dropped back and set his feet to throw – then launched a pass through the air. Frankie had run his **route** perfectly and was wide open.
I've got it, he thought as he sprinted under the ball.
A perfect pass! Frankie made the **reception** and kept running. Fifteen yard line….Ten…Five…

A ROUTE or *passing route* is run by a player looking to make a catch. Only players who are eligible receivers (not linemen) can run a route and receive a pass.

A RECEPTION is the successful catch of a forward pass. If the receiver fails to catch the ball inbounds, the pass is ruled *incomplete* and play is stopped.

10

Touchdown! Frankie crossed the goal line to score the first points of the game.

"Great pass, Seth!" said Frankie as the team mobbed him in the end zone.

The special teams unit came out on the field to attempt the **point after touchdown**.

A **TOUCHDOWN** occurs when the team with the ball crosses its goal line. Worth six points, touchdowns are the highest scoring play in football. After a touchdown, a team is given the chance at a **POINT AFTER TOUCHDOWN (P.A.T.)**

Would they go for an **extra point** or a **two-point conversion**? The center snapped the ball. The kicker booted the ball. Through the goalposts – it's good! The Stallions made the extra point and led the game 7-0.

A team can attempt a P.A.T to score an EXTRA POINT, also called a one-point conversion, by kicking the ball through the goal posts. Or, a team can attempt to score two points - a TWO-POINT CONVERSION - by either running or passing the ball into the end zone.

After the kickoff, the Stallions came out on defense. Frankie played the position of linebacker.

The Bandits snapped the ball. As the quarterback handed the ball to the running back, an offensive lineman charged toward Frankie to make a **block**.

A BLOCK is done by the offensive players to protect the player with the ball. A player can use his hands to push the defensive player away from where the ball carrier wants to go.

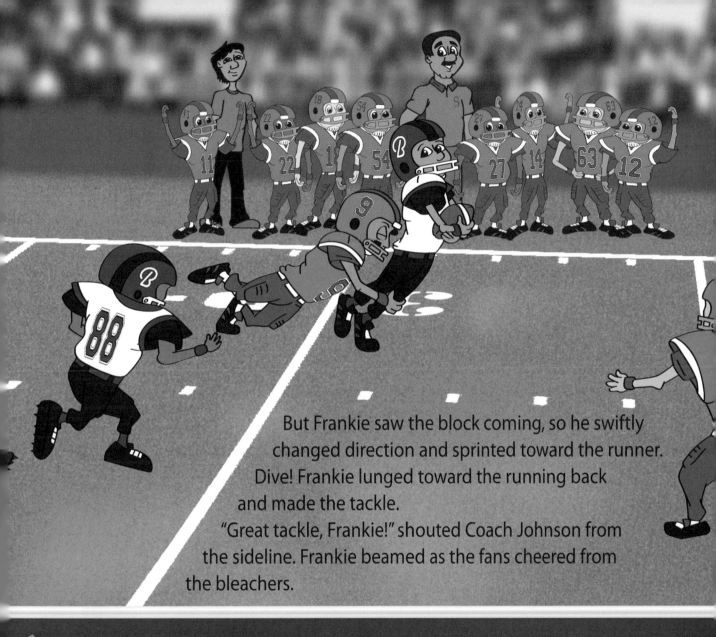

But Frankie saw the block coming, so he swiftly changed direction and sprinted toward the runner. Dive! Frankie lunged toward the running back and made the tackle.

"Great tackle, Frankie!" shouted Coach Johnson from the sideline. Frankie beamed as the fans cheered from the bleachers.

 QUICK TIP: On offense, a good blocker will recognize where the ball carrier wants to go and move his body into a defending player. Players on defense have the difficult job of watching both the player with the ball as well as the offensive blocking players.

Two plays later, it was third down. The Stallions were doing their best to make the Bandits **punt**, or even better - force a **turnover**. Frankie felt the tension rising as he lined up behind the defensive linemen.

A **PUNT** is a play in which the offense kicks the ball back to the other team – usually on 4th down. The *punter* will take the ball and drop-kick it as far down the field as he can while his teammates sprint down the field to tackle the other team's runner.

A *turnover on downs* can happen when a team fails to make a first down when going for it on fourth down.

The quarterback took the snap.
Passing play, Frankie thought as the quarterback stepped
back to pass.
Frankie saw the running back jet out of the backfield for a pass.
Would he get there in time?
Yes! The quarterback threw the ball, but Frankie made the **interception**.
He raced up the sideline with the ball, careful not to **fumble**,
and was tackled out of bounds.

A **TURNOVER** occurs when the defense takes the ball from the offense.
An **INTERCEPTION** happens when a pass is caught by the defensive team.
A **FUMBLE** happens when an offensive player drops the ball before he is down.
A fumble can be picked up by either the offense to keep possession or the defense
as a turnover.

Frankie grinned as he got up and high-fived Seth and Camden.

"Nice work, defense!" shouted Coach Johnson over the roars from the crowd.

The Stallions went back out on offense but could not get a first down.

After the punt, the Bandits drove down the field and kicked a **field goal**.

A FIELD GOAL is a scoring play worth three points in which a team kicks the ball through the goal posts above the crossbar. Making a field goal gives a team another way to score points if it is stopped short of a touchdown and is usually attempted on 4th down as long as the team is in *field goal range*.

Heading into **halftime**,
the Stallions led 7-3.
Coach Johnson smacked his players
on the shoulder pads.
"Let's go get 'em, boys!" and they took
the field for the second half.

HALFTIME comes at the midway point of every football game. The game is usually broken into four quarters, with halftime coming at the end of the second quarter.

The Bandits received the second half kickoff in the end zone, but the runner decided not to take the **touchback** and bolted out of the end zone. Frankie raced down the field to make the tackle.

The Bandits runner started one way, then turned and ran back toward Frankie's side. Frankie saw that he was near the goal line, so he darted in hoping to tackle the runner in the end zone for a **safety**.

A **TOUCHBACK** happens on a kickoff, punt, or interception when the ball goes into the end zone and is not returned by the offense. The ball is placed on the twenty yard line on a touchback

A **SAFETY** is when the offensive team gets tackled in its own end zone, except in a touchback situation. The defensive team is awarded 2 points for a safety, and

its opponent must kick the ball back to them on the following play.

Frankie reached out to make the tackle, but the running back broke free and scurried up the sideline until he was pushed out of bounds. "Nice try," said Seth as they huddled for the next play. "We'll get him next time."

 QUICK TIP: A tackling player should always keep his head up and use his shoulders to make the first contact with the ball carrier. Once the hit is made, he should quickly wrap his arms around the runner and drive him to the ground.

In the second half of the game, both teams struggled to make first downs. At the start of the fourth quarter, the Stallions still had the lead 7-3. The Bandits controlled the ball near mid-field. Frankie and Seth signaled the rest of their teammates to line up in a **man-to-man defense**.

MAN-TO-MAN DEFENSE is when each eligible receiver on the offensive team is covered by a linebacker or defensive back. This is different than a *zone* defense in which each defensive player is assigned an area of the field.

Fight!

The quarterback received the snap and made a **lateral toss** to the running back. Frankie and Seth charged from their positions to make the tackle. Suddenly, the running back set his feet to pass the ball. It was a trick play! He threw the ball downfield to a wide open receiver.

"Touchdown!" signaled the referee.

The Bandits now led the game 10-7.

A LATERAL TOSS or backward pass happens when a player throws the ball behind him to another teammate. Unlike forward passes, a team can throw as many lateral tosses as it wants on any given play. But players should be careful; backward passes are live balls if they hit the ground, and can be recovered as fumbles.

After the kickoff, Frankie's team drove the ball down the field. They needed a field goal to tie the game but were hoping for a touchdown as they neared the goal line.

"Second down, five yards to go for a touchdown," said Seth as they broke the huddle. But just as they prepared to snap the ball, one of the offensive linemen jumped out of his stance early and was called for a false-start **penalty**. This moved the ball back five yards.

A PENALTY is called on a team when one of its players breaks the rules. The referee signals the penalty by throwing a yellow flag on the field during the play. The ball is then moved forward or backward to punish the offending team.

See the glossary for a list of common penalties.

Then on third down, the Stallions' tight end was called for a holding penalty. This moved the ball so far from the goal line that the Stallions eventually had to kick the field goal on fourth down.

"That's okay, guys," Frankie said as they ran to the sideline after making the kick. "We've tied the game. Now we need to get the ball back and score again."

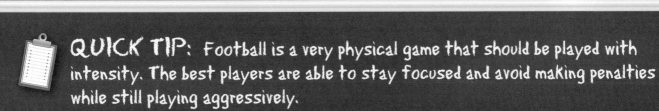

QUICK TIP: Football is a very physical game that should be played with intensity. The best players are able to stay focused and avoid making penalties while still playing aggressively.

With the score tied 10-10, Frankie returned to the field to play defense. It was third down. The clock ticked. The fans stood and cheered. With only a couple minutes left to play, Frankie's skin tingled with nervous anticipation as he felt the buzz of the stadium.

Frankie jumped out of his stance as the quarterback took the snap and went to hand the ball off to the running back. But no! It was a **play action** pass!

PLAY ACTION is when a team fakes one type of play and then runs another. Play action often happens when the quarterback fakes a hand-off to the running back and then attempts to pass the ball.

The Bandits' tight end had gotten behind him and was catching the pass. Frankie turned and sprinted after the receiver, finally catching him at the fifteen yard line.

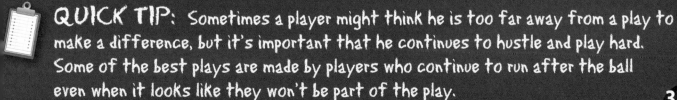

QUICK TIP: Sometimes a player might think he is too far away from a play to make a difference, but it's important that he continues to hustle and play hard. Some of the best plays are made by players who continue to run after the ball even when it looks like they won't be part of the play.

"I shouldn't have let him catch the ball," grumbled Frankie as he returned to the defensive huddle.

"We can still do this!" Seth said in the huddle. They glanced at the scoreboard - less than a minute left to play.

The Bandits tried two running plays but could not gain any yards. On third down, Frankie looked at Coach Johnson for the play call signal.

"Zone **blitz**," relayed Frankie. "Give it all you've got! Ready…Break!"

A **BLITZ** is a play in which the defensive team tries to rush more players at the quarterback than the offense can block. A well-timed blitz can help the defensive team tackle the offense in the backfield for a loss of yards.

Frankie glanced at the clock. Fifteen seconds left. Snap!
Frankie burst around the offensive line and dove at the quarterback for the **sack**.
"Fumble!" yelled the Stallions' sideline.

A SACK is when the quarterback is tackled behind the line of scrimmage for a loss of yards. A good quarterback will avoid getting sacked by throwing or running the ball before getting tackled in the backfield.

Frankie scooped up the ball.
"Run, Frankie!" Camden yelled. Frankie jetted up the field toward the end zone.

The Bandits players were closing in. He put his head down and kept running. *We'll win the game if I can make it*, he thought.

Fifty yard line...Forty...Thirty.

The crowd stood and cheered him on. Twenty-five….Twenty…Fifteen.

Frankie felt a hand clutching for his jersey. Ten…Five…

HOME 10 0:02 10 AWAY
QUARTER
****

Touchdown!
The game clock had expired during the play.
After tacking on the extra point, the Stallions won the game 17-10.
The players shook hands with their opponents.
"Great game," they said. "Well played!"

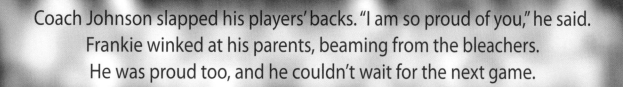

Coach Johnson slapped his players' backs. "I am so proud of you," he said.
Frankie winked at his parents, beaming from the bleachers.
He was proud too, and he couldn't wait for the next game.

About the Authors:

Gerald Hacker and his wife Amy live in Trussville, Alabama and are the parents of five children. An avid sports fan, Gerald has coached his children's teams in both baseball and basketball. During his years of coaching, Gerald realized the largest obstacle for children entering into youth sports was understanding the rules of the game. This led him to team up with his friend Andrew Wolthers to develop The Rules of the Game series.

Andrew Wolthers enjoyed numerous sports as a youth and played Division I basketball while a student at Northern Arizona University. Andrew coaches youth basketball and soccer throughout the year and currently resides in Hendersonville, Tennessee with his wife Lindsay and their two sons.

Ryan Adamson is an Illustrator and Cartoonist. He lives in Cincinnati, Ohio with his wife Cindy, their cats and two dogs. For better or worse, he's a fan of his hometown teams the Cincinnati Bengals and the Reds.